REVISE KEY STAGE 2 SATs
English

TARGETED PRACTICE SPELLING

Series Consultant: Janice Pimm

Author: Isabelle Bridger Eames

Also available:

Revise Key Stage 2 SATs English Targeted Practice
Grammar   9781292145945

Revise Key Stage 2 SATs English Targeted Practice
Reading   9781292145952

For the full range of Pearson revision titles, visit:
www.pearsonschools.co.uk/revise

Contents

A small bit of small print

The Standards and Testing Agency publishes Sample Test Materials on its website. This is the official content and this book should be used in conjunction with it. The questions in this book have been written to help you practise what you have learned in your revision. Remember: the real test questions may not look like this.

Introduction

About your tests

At the end of Year 6, you will take tests to find out about your English skills. This book will help you revise your **spelling** skills.

* There will be one **spelling** test. Your teacher will read 20 words out loud. You need to write down the correct spellings. This test will take about 15 minutes.

* You will also need to use your spelling skills in the **grammar** test. This test will ask you questions about spelling, punctuation and grammar. You will have 45 minutes to do this test.

There will be also be one **reading** test. Your teacher will look at some of your pieces of writing but there won't be a **writing** test.

Using this book

Each page of this book is about a different skill. Use the checkboxes at the top of the page to track your progress:

Had a go ☐ Tick this box when you've had a go at the page.

Nearly there ☐ Tick this box when you understand the page quite well.

Nailed it! ☐ Tick this box when you understand the page really well.

Root words

1. How many words can you find with the root word 'assist' in them?
   Write the words in the boxes. One has been done for you.

assistant

   5 marks

2. Use the prefixes and suffixes in the table to make as many words
   as you can from the root words 'observe' and 'tolerate'.
   Write your words in the middle of the table.
   One has been done for you.

   > A suffix is an ending added to a root word.

   > A prefix is a beginning added to a root word.

prefixes	observe	tolerate	suffixes
in-			-ed
			-ant
			-ance
un-	unobservant		-ing

   9 marks

3. a) Complete the passage with the words listed below.

unprovable   prove   disproved   approval

   The detective needed to .... that the accused man was

   guilty. The lawyer said the crime was .... In court, all was

   .... which gained the .... of the

   people watching.

   b) What is the root word? ....   **5 marks**

1

Double consonants

1. Make as many words as you can by adding the suffixes listed below to the words in the table. One has been done for you.

-er	-est	-ing	-ed

fit	fitter
begin	
forget	
label	

> Remember to double the final consonant.

10 marks

2. Circle the words that are spelled correctly.

pating	humming	playying	figting	droped
playing	dropped	huming	fighting	patting

5 marks

3. Use the correct form of the root words listed below to complete the sentences. One has been done for you.

~~run~~	jog	travel	label	shop

a) The ....runner.......... was .... with friends.

b) We are .... to Spain for our summer holiday.

c) Mummy was .... the presents she

had bought when she was ....

4 marks

2

Plurals

1. Some plural words end with -s and others end with -es. Put the words in the cloud in the correct column of the table. One has been done for you.

> A plural is more than one.

~~window~~ beach wish door cake banana shoe
cross waltz bus church

> Add 'es' to words ending in 'ch', 'sh', 's', 'ss', 'x' or 'z' to make the plural.

-s	-es
windows	

10 marks

2. a) Write the plurals of the words in the boxes.

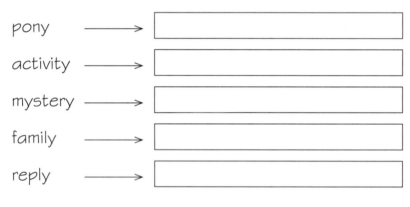

pony ⟶ ☐

activity ⟶ ☐

mystery ⟶ ☐

family ⟶ ☐

reply ⟶ ☐

> When the letter <u>before</u> a 'y' is a consonant, change the 'y' to an 'i' before adding 'es'.

5 marks

b) What do each of the plural forms you have written have in common?

.... **1 mark**

3. Circle the correct spellings of the words in the sentences.

a) The *knives/knivs* were in the draw.

b) The *citys/cities* were in the north of the country.

2 marks

Possessive apostrophes with plurals

1. Rewrite the phrases, using the possessive apostrophe. One has been done for you.

   > You use an apostrophe to show that something belongs to someone.

   a) the spaceship belonging to the alien

   the alien's spaceship
   ....

   b) the spaceship belonging to the aliens

   ....

   c) the bat belonging to the girl

   ....

   d) the bat belonging to the girls

   .... **3 marks**

2. Circle the correct word to complete the sentences.

   a) The *childrens'/childrens/children's* classroom was very tidy.

   b) The *boys/boy's/boys'* toilets were cleaned every night.
          2 marks

3. Rewrite the sentences, using the possessive apostrophe.

   a) Joe hung up the saddles belonging to the horses.

   ....

   b) The cat sniffed at the cheese belonging to the mice.

   ....
          2 marks

4. Add plural possessive apostrophes to correct the sentences.

   a) The dogs toys were lined up next to one another.

   b) The trees leaves danced in the wind.   **2 marks**

Contractions

1. Circle the correct uncontracted form of the contracted words in the table. One has been done for you.

contracted	uncontracted
i'll	i am (i will) we will
isn't	is not i am has not
shan't	will not shall not could not
won't	do not will not shall not

The apostrophes must show exactly where the letters are missing.

3 marks

2. Write the contracted form of each of the words listed below.

could not	have not	you are

.... **3 marks**

3. Circle the correctly spelled contractions listed below.

we're   should'nt   theyr'e   he'll

h'ell   wouldn't   wa'snt   they're

wasn't   shouldn't   wer'e   would'nt   **6 marks**

4. Complete the sentences below with the contracted from of the words in brackets.

a) "(We will) .... wash the dishes!" The children exclaimed in unison.

b) "I (cannot) .... do it!" shouted the girl in frustration.

c) "It (might not) .... rain this afternoon" said Mum.   **3 marks**

Using hyphens

1. Rewrite the words below including the correct hyphens.

   a) coordinate ....

   b) reenter ....

   c) cooperate ....

   d) coown ....

   > Hyphens are often used to separate vowels: one on the root word and one on the prefix, e.g. re-apply.

   4 marks

2. Underline the words in the sentences that should have a hyphen.

   a) The city was very built up.

   b) It was a very well known piece of music.

   c) The wax models were very life like.

   d) She had a great relationship with her mother in law.   **4 marks**

3. Write a sentence using the hyphenated word 'ice-skate'.

   ....   **1 mark**

4. Draw lines to match the two parts of the hyphenated word.

fair		-war
pre		-catching
quick		-haired
eye		-thinking
re		-purpose
multi		-establish

   6 marks

The 'ei after c' rule

1. Circle each of the words listed below that is spelled correctly.

   decieve   deceive

   conceive   concieve

   recieve   receive

> The 'ei after c' rule usually applies when the sound is **'ee'**.

3 marks

2. Complete the words with the missing letters in the sentences.

   a) The top of the Christmas tree touched the c_ _ling.

   b) The ch_ _f inspector was interviewing the suspect.

> The 'ei after c' rule applies when the 'c' is the letter directly before the **'ei'**.

2 marks

3. Draw lines to match each word with its meaning.

word	meaning
perceive	dishonesty or lying
conceit	recognise or identify something
deceit	self-importance or vanity.

3 marks

4. Unscramble the following words and write the correct spellings.

   a) ceptier .... (proof of receiving)

   b) isiefchm .... (trouble)

   c) cctedonei .... (big-headed)

3 marks

5. Write the missing letters into the words below.

   a) financ_ _r

   b) spec_ _s

   c) anc_ _nt

> Be careful with these words. They are tricky!

3 marks

Prefixes: un- and de-

1. Complete the table with the words listed below.
   One has been done for you.

> A prefix is a group of letters 'fixed' (added) to the beginning of a word.

~~well~~   acceleration   dressed   healthy   allocate   bag

words with the prefix 'un'	words with the prefix 'de'
well	

5 marks

2. Circle each word that uses the prefix 'un' correctly.

unshort	unclip	unhelpful	ungreen
unbutton	unlong	unthin	unpack

4 marks

3. Use the prefix 'un' or 'de' to complete the words in the sentences.

   a) The member wanted to ....activate her account.

   b) I am determined to ....clutter this messy house.

   c) Mina needs to ....flea her dog.

   d) The story was a lie. It was ....true.

   e) Michael felt very ....fortunate to have missed the flight.   **5 marks**

Prefixes: im-, in-, il-, ir-

1. Draw lines to match each prefix with the correct word.

prefix	word
im	correct
in	legal
il	responsible
ir	possible

All of these prefixes reverse the meaning of the root word that they are attached to.

4 marks

2. Circle the words that are spelled correctly.

inactive   imactive

inrelevant   irrelevant

illegible   imlegible

impatient   impatent

Generally add 'il' before the letter 'l' and add 'ir' before the letter 'r'.

4 marks

3. Use the words listed below to complete the sentences.

immature	irrelevant	imperfect	irregular

a) It is an .... world.

b) The shape was an .... pentagon.

c) She was a kind girl though a bit ....

d) The teacher glared as she said the comment was

completely ....

Generally add 'im' before letters 'm' and 'p'

4 marks

9

Prefixes: auto-, bi-, tri-

1. Draw lines to match each prefix with its meaning.

prefix

| auto |
| bi |
| tri |

meaning

| two |
| three |
| self |

3 marks

2. Use the correct prefix to complete the words in the sentences below.

a) She wrote an ....biography about herself.

b) The flower show was a ....annual event – every two years.

c) It was an ....matic car.

d) She was ....lingual because she spoke French, German and Spanish.

4 marks

3. Draw lines to match each prefix to its correct word.

prefix

| auto |
| bi |
| tri |

word

| scuit |
| mobile |
| cycle |

The 'bi' at the beginning of the word biscuits comes from the two-step process originally used to cook them.

3 marks

More prefixes

1. Draw lines to match each prefix with the correct meaning.

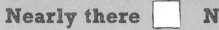

Never change the spelling of the root word when you add a prefix.

prefix	meaning
sub	against/opposite
inter	above/beyond
super	under/below
anti	between/together

4 marks

2. Circle the real words in the list below.

subheading   submarine   antiheading   interact

intermarine   anitact   substar   superstar   4 marks

3. Add the correct prefixes to compete the words in the sentences.

   a) He took the fast ....city train from Bristol to London.

   b) She needed to ....merge her head in the water.

   c) "Can you get me some milk from the ....market?" asked Dad.

   d) "Jog in an ....clockwise direction around the hall," said the gym instructor.   4 marks

4. Draw lines to match each prefix to the correct word.

prefix	word
sub	natural
inter	septic
super	divide
anti	national

4 marks

Endings: -able and -ible

1. Circle the correctly spelled words listed below.

commendible   commendable

horrable   horrible

adorible   adorable

forcible   forcable

possable   possible

reliable   relible

> Use the ending -able if the root word doesn't change e.g. consider → consider<u>able</u>.

6 marks

2. Use -able or -ible to complete the words in the sentences.

a) The writing was very neat and leg………………………..

b) Going to the fair was very enjoy………………………..

c) It was a terr……………………… journey as they were stuck in traffic on the motorway for hours.

> Use the ending -ible if you have to change the root word.

d) They won a consider……………………… amount of money on the lottery.

4 marks

3. Draw lines to match the start of each word to its correct ending.

word	ending
toler	ible
applic	able
vis	ible
incred	able

4 marks

Endings: -ibly and -ably

1. Turn the adjectives into adverbs. One has been done for you.

adjective	adverb
adorable	adorably
noticeable	
considerable	
tolerable	

3 marks

2. Add the correct endings to complete the words in the sentences.

   a) It all went horr............................. wrong.

   b) It was poss............................. the best day that Niamh had ever had.

   c) It was incred............................. warm down by the swimming pool.   **3 marks**

3. Circle the correctly spelled words listed below.

   capibly   capably

   laughibly   laughably

   honourably   honouribly

   irritibly   irritably   **4 marks**

4. Write a sentence using the word 'sensibly'.

   ....   **1 mark**

5. Unscramble the following words and write the correct spelling.

   a) lyminaboab .... (dreadful)

   b) mirabadly .... (excellent)

   c) rgaulyab .... (to make a point)

   d) ponirrsibesly .... (not trustworthy)

   e) possimibly .... (no way)   **5 marks**

> Work out the ending of each word and then look at the remaining letters. Use a scrap piece of paper to jot ideas down.

Endings: -tion, -sion, -cian, -ssion

1. Turn the verbs into nouns by adding -sion. One has been done for you.

verbs	nouns
expand	expansion
extend	
comprehend	

> The ending -sion goes with words that end -nd.

2 marks

2. Turn the verbs into nouns by adding -ssion.
   One has been done for you.

verbs	nouns
express	expression
discuss	
admit	
permit	

> -ssion is generally for words that end with -mit or -ss.

3 marks

3. Add the correct endings to complete the words in the sentences.

   a) The musi.......................... played the violin beautifully.

> The ending -cian is given to words that are the name of a job e.g. electrician.

> -tion is the most common word ending.

   b) The comple .... date for the
   coursework was 5th October.

2 marks

Endings: -ant and -ent

1. Circle the correctly spelled words listed below.

relevant   relevent

expectent   expectant

tolerent   tolerant

hesitant   hesitent

4 marks

2. Turn the nouns into adjectives. One has been done for you.

nouns	adjectives
observance	observant
expectance	
frequency	
innocence	

An adjective is a word that describes a noun.

3 marks

3. Use the words listed below to complete the sentences.

assistant	confident	obedient

a) Sharon delivered the speech in a .... manner.

b) The shop .... took the money for the bread.

c) The dog was very ....

3 marks

4. Write the correct ending -ant or -ent to these words.

a) contest..........................

b) immin..........................

c) reluc..........................

d) pres..........................

e) intellig..........................

f) defi..........................

6 marks

Endings: -cial and -tial

1. Circle the correct spellings in the pairs of words in the passage below.

   It was a very *spectial/special* occasion. There were many *official/offitial* looking people in the building. It was *crucial/crutial* that they made the right decision.

   > The ending -cial tends to follow a vowel. The ending -tial tends to follow a consonant. Remember there are exceptions.

   3 marks

2. Circle the correct spellings in the pairs of words in the passage below.

   Essencial/Essential road works were being carried out in the *residencial/residential* area. It meant that there was much *potential/potencial* for *substantial/substancial* delays.

   4 marks

3. Write the root words listed below with the correct ending in the table. One has been done for you.

   | ~~face~~   artifice   resident   benefit   president   race   sacrifice |

-cial ending	-tial ending
facial	

   6 marks

4. Circle the correct spelling in the pairs of words in the sentences.

   a) They had an important *financial/finantial* decision to make.

   b) The private meeting was *confidencial/confidential*.

   c) Sally was a very *sotial/social* person as she loved to talk to other people.

   d) The evidence was only *circumstantial/circumstancial*.

   4 marks

Endings: -tious and -cious

1. Draw lines to match each noun to the correct adjective.

noun

grace

space

malice

adjective

spacious

malicious

gracious

> The ending -cious is often used with words ending in -ce and means 'full of'.

3 marks

2. Turn the nouns listed below into adjectives and write them in the correct column in the table. One has been done for you.

~~nutrition~~   caution   suspicion   ambition

-tious	-cious
nutritious	

> The ending -tious is often used with words ending in -tion and means 'full of'.

3 marks

3. Circle all the words that are spelled correctly in the list below.

vicious	vitious
pretious	precious
conscious	contious
delitious	delicious
malicious	malitious
fictitious	ficticious

6 marks

Endings: -al, -el and -le

1. Circle all the words that are spelled correctly in the list below.

metel   metal

pedal   pedel

hospital   hospitel

animal   animel   **4 marks**

2. Add the correct endings (-al, -el or -le) to complete the words.

a) Can I have an app_ _?

b) The Houses of Parliament are in the capit_ _.

c) I felt like I was in the midd_ _.

d) The new baby was very litt_ _.

e) They have a swimming pool in their hot_ _.   **5 marks**

3. Use the words listed below to complete the sentences.

camel   table   bottle

a) They ate their meal around a large ....

b) When the .... was opened the fizzy drink sprayed all over
the floor.

c) The .... had two humps.   **3 marks**

4. Circle the correct spelling in the pairs of words in the
sentences below.

a) The train was scheduled to *travel/travle* down the very
long *tunnel/tunnal* at exactly 0300 hours.

b) The *squirrel/squirral* scampered up the tree away from
the approaching cat.

c) The *towal/towel* danced and waved in the wind as it
dried on the washing line.

4 marks

Endings: -ant and -ent

1. Draw lines to match each word to its correct meaning.

word

| accident |

| experiment |

| different |

meaning

| test or trial |

| diverse or dissimilar |

| mishap |

3 marks

2. Circle the correct spelling in each pair of words in the sentences below.

a) The *innocent/innocant* man was freed from prison.

b) Alice was upgraded to first class as she was a *frequent/frequant* flyer.

c) The protesters were calling for a *decent/decant* wage.   **3 marks**

3. Complete the words in the sentences.

a) She was confid.......................... that her secret would remain safe.

b) Mohammed was abs.......................... from today's lesson.

c) Jasmine enjoyed being a contest.......................... on the game show.

d) They looked at the transpar.......................... water in the glass.

e) The patient was reluct.......................... to go to hospital..   **5 marks**

4. Write three sentences. Each sentence must include one of the words listed below.

| abundant   defiant   distant |

....

....

....   **3 marks**

Endings: -ance and -ence

1. Change the adjectives in the table that end -ant to nouns ending -ance. One has been done for you.

adjective	noun
abundant	abundance
arrogant	
assistant	
fragrant	
important	

4 marks

2. Change the adjectives in the table that end -ent to nouns ending -ence. One has been done for you.

adjective	noun
absent	absence
adolescent	
competent	
confident	
dependent	

4 marks

3. Circle the correct spelling in the pairs of words in the sentences below.

a) The *silence/silnce* was golden and they all revelled in it.

b) His outward *appearance/appearence* was extremely smart.

c) The *circumferance/circumference* of the circle measured exactly one metre.

3 marks

4. Write a sentence using the adjective of the verb 'to remember'.

.... **1 mark**

5. Write the correct ending -ance or -ence to these words.

a) clear...........................

b) abs.........................

c) accept...........................

d) consequ...........................

e) guid...........................

5 marks

20

Endings: -ancy and -ency

1. Turn the words ending in -ation into related words ending -ancy.

words ending in -ation	related words ending -ancy
hesitation	
expectation	

2 marks

2. Turn the words ending -ant into nouns ending -ancy.

words ending in -ant	related words ending -ancy
pregnant	
accountant	
flippant	

3 marks

3. Turn the words ending -ent into nouns ending -ency.

words ending in -ent	related words ending -ency
absorbent	
consistent	
decent	

> Words that have a soft 'c' or soft 'qu' in them often end with —ency e.g. de**c**ency, fre**qu**ency.

3 marks

4. Circle the correct spelling in the pairs of words in the sentences below.

a) There was a *vacency/vacancy* in the hotel.

b) There was a problem with *truancy/truency* at the school.

c) The company claimed to have greatly improved the *efficiancy/efficiency* of the car.

3 marks

5. Write the correct ending -ancy or -ency to these words.

a) discrep.........................

b) ag.........................

c) inf.........................

d) redund.........................

e) curr.........................

5 marks

Endings: -sure, -ture and -cher

1. Circle the correctly spelled words listed below.

picher	picture
nacher	nature
adventure	advanture
measure	mesure

4 marks

2. Draw lines to match the start of the word with its correct ending.

word part

crea

ar

enclo

word ending

-sure

-ture

-cher

> The ending '-cher' means the doer of something e.g teacher.

3 marks

3. Write the correct word endings in the sentences below.

a) X marked the trea_ _ _ _ on the pirate's map.

b) "It was a plea_ _ _ _ doing business with you!" said the business woman.

c) The shop was full of antique furni_ _ _ _ .

3 marks

4. Write three sentences. Each sentence must include one word listed below.

texture   exposure   preacher

....

....

.... **3 marks**

22

Endings: -ly

1. Turn the underlined adjectives into adverbs by adding -ly. One has been done for you.

   Samantha was <u>rude.</u> Samantha spoke **rudely.**

   Omar was <u>gentle</u> with the cat. Omar stroked the cat ....

   Kelvin felt <u>cheerful</u> as he walked home. Kelvin walked home ....

   2 marks

2. Add -ly to the adjectives to make adverbs. One has been done for you.

adjectives	adverbs
happy	**happily**
funny	
frisky	
heroic	
basic	
dramatic	
simple	
humble	
noble	

   8 marks

3. Draw lines to match each word with the correct ending.

   root word   ending

frantic		ly
complete		ily
angr		ally

   3 marks

4. Unscramble the words and write the correct spellings.

   a) dlsay .... (unhappily)

   b) ilgryump .... (in a bad mood)

   c) ylbeluaufit .... (good looking)

   3 marks

Endings: -ous

1. Add the suffix -ous to the nouns to create adjectives.

nouns	adjectives
danger	
joy	
courage	
nerve	

> A suffix is 'fixed' (added) to the end of a word to make a new word.

4 marks

2. Circle the correctly spelled words.

spontanious   spontaneous

vigorous   vigerous

outrageous   outraegous

sereous   serious

4 marks

3. Use the correct form of the word in brackets to complete the sentence.

   a) The film that I am watching with my friends is

   quite funny. It is (humour) ....

> Words ending in -our need to be modified before adding -ous.

   b) The popstar was extremely (glamour) ....

2 marks

4. Draw lines to match each word to its correct synonym.

word	synonym
famous	different
various	great
tremendous	huge
enormous	well-known

4 marks

24

Endings: -ation

1. Write the words below in alphabetical order.

| information | adoration | sensation | preparation | admiration |

.... **1 mark**

2. Add the ending -ation to complete the words in the table.
   One has been done for you.

lubric-	**lubrication**	imagin-	
civilis-		consider-	
veget-		punctu-	

5 marks

3. Use the correct form of the word in brackets to complete the sentence.

   a) The food (prepare)........................... took the
   longest.

   b) They completed the (register) ....
   form online.

   c) The Queen's (coronate) .... was
   a momentous occasion.

3 marks

4. Draw lines to match each word to its correct synonym.

word	synonym
location	country
nation	party
celebration	position
donation	contribution

4 marks

Adding suffixes to words ending in -fer

1. Rewrite the words adding the suffix -ed.

prefer = [_____]

refer = [_____]

transfer = [_____]

> Double the 'r' here when adding -ing or -ed.

3 marks

2. Rewrite the words adding the suffix -ing.

prefer = [_____]

refer = [_____]

transfer = [_____]

3 marks

3. Rewrite the words adding the suffix -ence.

prefer = [_____]

refer = [_____]

transfer = [_____]

> Do not double the 'r' here when adding -ence.

3 marks

4. Draw lines to match each word in the list below to its correct meaning.

word	meaning
buffer	contrast
differ	bumper
infer	proposal
offer	suppose

4 marks

Adding suffixes to longer words

1. Add -ing to the root words to create new words.

root word	add -ing
forget	
begin	
garden	
limit	

Remember to learn which words double their final consonant when adding -ing.

4 marks

2. Add -ed to the root words to create new words.

root word	add -ed
admire	
allow	
inquire	
create	

Words which end in -e often lose the -e before adding -ed.

4 marks

3. Write three sentences. Each sentence must include one of the words listed below.

forgotten   controlled   decorative

....

....

.... 3 marks

4. Use the correct form of the word in brackets to complete the sentence.

a) There was a (disturb) .... in the neighbourhood.

b) The (journal) .... asked many questions for her newspaper article.

c) The (narrate) .... set the scene for the play.

d) There was (thunder) .... applause from the audience.   **4 marks**

More suffixes

1. Add the correct suffix -ful or -ness to the root words listed below.

   sad → ....

   play → ....

   hope → ....

   happy → ....

   shy → ....   5 marks

2. Draw lines to match each word to its correct suffix.

word	suffix
enjoy	ful
care	ness
plain	ment

                                                                    3 marks

3. Use the correct form of the word in brackets to complete the sentence.

   a) The food on the table was (plenty) ....

   b) The woman was left (penny) .... after her business failed.

   c) The wedding was a (joy) .... event.

   d) The older man was proud of his (bald) ....   4 marks

4. Write the correct spelling of the underlined words in the sentences.

   a) Kristy was extremely <u>basshful</u>. ....

   b) The <u>carmness</u> of the sea was very relaxing. ....

   c) The cat stalked the garden with <u>causiousness</u>. .... 3 marks

Homophones

1. Circle the correct homophone in each sentence.

   a) The toddler began to cry and *bawl/ball* because he had dropped his toy on the floor.

   b) The dog, Fido, was looking for a good spot to *berry/bury* his bone.

   c) The reviewer said it was a *great/grate* show with some fantastic performances.

   d) Simon let out a huge *groan/grown* when he saw the mess in the kitchen.

   e) We have no *meet/meat* for our evening meal on Monday every week.   **5 marks**

2. Complete the sentences with the correct homophone shown in brackets.

   a) The (*mail/male*) .... was always delivered by 1pm.

   b) Do you (*here/hear*) .... the wind whistling in the trees?

   c) The captain examined the (*not/knot*) .... and could see that it was expertly tied.

   d) The (*main/mane*) .... course was chicken and chips.

   Homophone means 'one sound'.

   e) Have you seen the (*weather/whether*) .... forecast for the weekend?   **5 marks**

3. Circle the homophones that are verbs and underline homophones that are nouns. One has been done for you.

Jasmine was always (led) by her gut feeling.	Lead is a metal that was in pencils.
The past can be difficult to remember.	I passed my driving test on Tuesday.
Suzie guessed the final answer on the quiz and got it right!	Michael was a perfect house guest.
The mist descended on the valley.	I am so sorry that I missed your birthday.

3 marks

Silent letters

1. Read the passage and circle all of the silent letters.

   The knight pulled the knife from his knee. Could it be – he thought solemnly – that he was stuck on this ghastly island?

   > Read the sentence out loud to help you spot the silent letters.

   8 marks

2. Write four sentences. Each sentence must include one of the words listed below.

doubt	island	lamb	thistle

   ....

   ....

   ....

   .... 4 marks

3. Complete the words with the missing silent letters.

   colum _ (tall pillar)

   w _ at (a question word)

   w _ istle (blown at full time)

   shou _ d (must)   4 marks

4. Unscramble the following words and write the correct spellings.

   a) umnaut .... (season)

   b) eswedanay .... (day of the week)

   c) ssorssci .... (tool for cutting)

   d) dorsw .... (weapon)

   e) iroch .... (group of people singing)

   f) estgu .... (visitor)   6 marks

Words with 'ei', 'eigh' or 'ey'

1. Circle the letter strings: 'ei', 'eigh' or 'ey' in the words below.

    vein   weigh   eight   neighbour   they   **5 marks**

2. Complete the table with the words listed below in the correct column for their letter string: 'ei', 'eigh' or 'ey'. One has been done for you.

~~rein~~   reign   freight   sheikh   grey   prey   weight   veil

'ei'	'eigh'	'ey'
rein		

                                               7 marks

3. Complete the words using the letter string 'ei', 'eigh' or 'ey'.

    a) Rules are there to ob...........................

    b) Please conv........................... the message correctly.

    c) The carpet in the bedroom is a b...........................ge colour.

    d) The sl........................... flew down the white hill that was covered in snow.   **4 marks**

4. Draw lines to match each word with the correct meaning.

                 word   word meaning

word		word meaning
survey		carries blood to heart
vein		noise a horse makes
neigh		questionnaire
eight		half of 16

                                                     4 marks

Words with 'y'

1. Draw lines to match the missing word in these sentences.

sentence	word
The story of Medusa is a...	Egypt.
Shanaz did twenty bench presses at the...	mystery.
The River Nile is in...	myth.
Simon was determined to solve the...	Pyramid.
The Seven Wonders of the World include the Great...	gym.

5 marks

2. Complete the sentences with the words listed below.

symbol	dynasty	synagogue	mystic

a) A .... is a period of years in which a certain pharaoh, king, queen or family is in control of the lands.

b) The tomb was full of .... artefacts and relics.

c) This .... means equal: =.

d) Jewish people worship in a ....　**4 marks**

3. Circle the correctly spelled words.

himn　　　　　　　hymn

synonym　　　　　synonim

crypt　　　　　　　cript

cygnet　　　　　　cygnat

cristal　　　　　　crystal　　　　　　**5 marks**

4. Write the correct spelling of the underlined words in the sentences below.

a) He forgot the <u>lirics</u> in the middle of singing the song. ....

b) Water is made up of <u>oxigen</u> and hydrogen. ....　**2 marks**

32

Words with 'ough'

1. Write the words listed below with the same sound in the table.
   One has been done for you.

bought	tough	although	~~thorough~~	through	cough
rough	plough	ought	though		

'ough' sound	words with that sound
like 'a' in above	thorough
like 'o' in go	
like 'oo' in too	
like 'off' in offer	
like 'uff' in suffer	
like 'ow' in flower	
like 'aw' in saw	

9 marks

2. Complete the sentences with the words listed below.

fought	enough	dough	through

a) Have you had .... for breakfast?

b) Knead the .... for ten minutes.

c) They .... hard to win the match.

d) Walk .... the park and then turn right.

4 marks

3. Correct the spelling mistakes in the sentences below.

a) I thawt .... the film would never end.

b) Nawt .... is a number between −1 and 1.

c) I brawt .... the post card my Auntie sent me from
   America into school to show my friends.

3 marks

Words with 'ei' or 'ie'

1. Use the words listed below to complete the sentences.

ancient	efficient	sufficient	conscience

a) An .... engine works well.

b) Do you have a clear ....?

c) Greece has many .... ruins.

d) Do you have .... money for lunch?   **4 marks**

2. Complete the words in the sentences with 'ei' or 'ie'.

a) Guards – s......ze these men!

b) I love walking through the f......lds in the summer.

c) I can speak three for......gn languages.

d) Help! Stop that th......f!   **4 marks**

3. Circle the correct spelling in the pairs of words in the sentences.

The *chief/chief* officer in charge of the incident spoke to the reporters.

We are having very *weird/wierd* weather.

A balanced diet should contain *protien/protein*.   **3 marks**

4. Draw lines to match each word to its correct meaning.

word	meaning
sovereign	give up
counterfeit	one or the other
either	fake or forged
forfeit	supreme ruler
leisure	free time

5 marks

Words with 'ou'

1. Use the words listed below to complete the sentences.

young	touch	double	trouble

   a) The sign read: Do not .... the artefacts.

   b) Mum said, 'Stay out of ....'

   c) Sadiq was too .... to go on the rollercoaster.

   d) Michelle wanted to .... her score next time.   **4 marks**

2. Draw lines to match each word to its correct meaning.

   word   meaning

   | tough | | bravery |

   | couple | | rough or hard |

   | enough | | plenty |

   | courage | | two | **4 marks**

3. Correct the spelling mistakes in the sentences below.

   a) The sea was very <u>rouff</u>. ....

   b) My <u>cusin</u> ....is called Catherine.

   c) We <u>encuraged</u> ....Sian to finish the race.

   d) He will <u>flurish</u> .... at his new school.

   e) We have to feed and water the plants to

   <u>nurish</u> .... them.   **5 marks**

35

Words with 'gue' or 'que'

1. Use the word beginnings below with the correct ending for the word in the table to write full words. One has been done for you.

| anti- | ~~lea~~ | ton- | uni- | ro- | pla- |

words ending 'gue'	words ending 'que'
league	

> Words ending with 'gue' and 'que' come from the French language.

5 marks

2. Add the correct endings to complete the words in the sentences.

a) There was a catalo.......................... of mistakes.

b) Marcy signed the che...........................

c) They used a new techni...........................

d) They told the story through dialo...........................   **4 marks**

3. Draw lines to match each word to its correct meaning.

word   meaning

monologue		not transparent
opaque		beautiful
vague		speech by one person
picturesque		unclear in meaning	**4 marks**

4. Circle the correctly spelled words.

intrigue	intrique
leaque	league
unigue	unique
grotesque	grotesgue

4 marks

Words with 'sc'

1. Complete the sentences with the words listed below.

science	scene	discipline	fascinate	crescent

a) The school was extremely strict on ....

b) The class were studying biology in ....

c) The Hugh Family lived at 152 Hilperton ....

d) It was a beautiful ....

e) She knew the ant farm would ....
   the children.

> All words with 's' spelled 'sc' originate from Latin.

5 marks

2. Draw lines to match each word to its correct meaning.

word	meaning
obscene	follower
transcend	to go beyond or above
adolescent	teenager
disciple	rude or indecent

4 marks

3. Complete the sentences with the correct spelling of the underlined words.

a) Now, we must <u>desend</u> .... the mountain.

b) Always carry <u>scisors</u> .... carefully.

c) What a beautiful <u>sented</u> .... candle.

d) Malik was eating protein to help build his <u>musles</u> ....

e) The boy had a large <u>absess</u> ....in his mouth.

f) The <u>assent</u> .... grew steeper.

6 marks

Words with 'ch'

1. Complete the sentences with the words listed below.

| ache | chaos | monarch | anchor |

a) Food poisoning can give you a stomach ....

b) The ship dropped .... in the port.

c) The change in timetable caused ....
at the dog show.

d) .... is another word for king or queen.

4 marks

2. Draw lines to match each word to its correct meaning.

word	meaning
orchid	building designer
architect	a type of flower
stomach	group of musicians
orchestra	organ in the body

4 marks

3. Circle the correctly spelled words.

skeme	scheme
chemistry	kemistry
mekanic	mechanic
teknical	technical
technology	teknology

5 marks

Tricky spellings

1. Draw lines to match each word to its correct meaning.

word	meaning
argument	related to money
initial	disagreement
financial	first

3 marks

2. Complete the sentences with the words listed below.

wholly	attention	provincial

a) It was a very .... town.

b) 'That behaviour was .... inappropriate!' said the Head.

c) Everyone's .... was on the boy at the front.   3 marks

3. Write four sentences. Each sentence must contain one of the words listed below.

rhythm	commercial	duly	intention

....

....

....

....   4 marks

4. Circle the correct spellings of the words below.

a) commercial/commertial

b) truely/truly

c) duly/dulely

d) intention/intenshion

> Tricky words need to be individually learned.

4 marks

39

Acrostics

You can use an **acrostic** to help you remember a tricky spelling. Take each of the letters of the spelling and create a memorable phrase to remind you of their order.

1. Make up your own acrostics for these words. One has been done for you.

a)

R	hythm
H	elps
Y	our
T	wo
H	ips
M	ove

b)

T	
O	
L	
E	
R	
A	
N	
T	

2. Choose another 'tricky' word that you have learned in this workbook. Write it below and make up your own acrostic for it.

40

Look, say, cover, write, check

Another good way to practise spellings is to: look, say, cover, write, check. You look at the word, say the word, cover the word, write the word while it is covered and then check if you have spelled the word correctly.

1. Try the 'look, say, cover, write, check' method for the words below.

word	write the word	check
possible		
acceleration		

2. Choose your own 'tricky' words that you have learned in this workbook. Write the words in the table below and try the 'look, say, cover, write, check' method.

word	write the word	check

Remember, practice makes perfect! Well done for all the practice you have done in this workbook!

Try using different colours when writing your spellings. Why not use one colour for all of the vowels and a different colour for all of the consonants?

Answers

SPELLING PATTERNS

1 Root words

1. Examples: assistance, assistantship, assisted, assistant, assisting, assists, co-assist, co-assisted, co-assisting, unassisted

2. Examples:
   Observe: observed, observant, observance, observing
   Tolerate: tolerated, tolerant, tolerance, tolerating, intolerant

3. a) prove, unprovable, disproved, approval
   b) prove

2 Double consonants

1. Examples: **Fit**: fittest, fitting, fitted
   Begin: beginner, beginning
   Forget: forgetter, forgetting
   Label: labeller, labelling, labelled

2. humming, fighting, playing, dropped, patting

3. a) jogging b) travelling c) labelling, shopping

3 Plurals

1. -s: doors, cakes, bananas, shoes
   -es: beaches, wishes, crosses, waltzes, buses, churches

2. a) ponies, activities, mysteries, families, replies
   b) They all have 'ies' endings.

3. a) knives b) cities

4 Possessive apostrophes with plurals

1. b) the aliens' spaceship c) the girl's bat d) the girls' bat

2. a) children's b) boys'

3. a) Joe hung up the horses' saddles.
   b) The cat sniffed at the mice's cheese.

4. a) dogs' b) trees'

5 Contractions

1. is not, shall not, will not

2. couldn't, haven't, you're

3. we're, he'll, wouldn't, they're, wasn't, shouldn't

4. a) we'll b) can't c) mightn't

6 Using hyphens

1. a) co-ordinate b) re-enter c) co-operate d) co-own

2. a) built-up b) well-known c) life-like d) mother-in-law

3. Example: On Saturday, the girls liked to ice-skate.

4. fair-haired, pre-war, quick-thinking,
   eye-catching, re-establish, multi-purpose

7 The 'ei after c' rule

1. deceive, conceive, receive

2. a) ceiling b) chief

3. perceive → recognise or identify something
   conceit → self-importance or vanity
   deceit → dishonesty or lying

4. a) receipt b) mischief c) conceited

5. a) financier b) species c) ancient

WORD BEGINNINGS

8 Prefixes: un- and de-

1. **un-**: dressed, healthy
   de-: acceleration, allocate, bag

2. unclip, unhelpful, unbutton, unpack

3. a) deactivate b) declutter c) deflea d) untrue
   e) unfortunate

9 Prefixes: im-, in-, il-, ir-

1. impossible, incorrect, illegal, irresponsible

2. inactive, illegible, irrelevant, impatient

3. a) imperfect b) irregular c) immature d) irrelevant

10 Prefixes: Prefixes: auto-, bi-, tri-

1. auto → self, bi → two, tri → three

2. a) autobiography b) biannual c) automatic d) trilingual

3. automobile, biscuit, tricycle

11 More prefixes

1. sub → under / below, inter → between / together
   super → above / beyond, anti → against / opposite

2. subheading, submarine, interact, superstar

3. a) intercity b) submerge c) supermarket d) anticlockwise

4. subdivide, international, superman, antiseptic

WORD ENDINGS

12 Endings: -able and -ible

1. commendable, horrible, adorable, forcible, possible,
   reliable

2. a) legible b) enjoyable c) terrible d) considerable

3. applicable, tolerable, visible, incredible

13 Endings: -ibly and -ably

1. noticeably, considerably, tolerably

2. a) horribly b) possibly c) incredibly

3. capably, laughably, honourably, irritably

4. Example: He sensibly tidied the cloakroom.

5. a) abominably b) admirably c) arguably d) irresponsibly
   e) impossibly

14 Endings: -tion -sion -cian -ssion

1. extension, comprehension

2. discussion, admission, permission

3. a) musician b) completion

15 Endings: -ant and -ent

1. relevant, expectant, hesitant, tolerant

2. expectant, frequent, innocent

3. a) confident b) assistant c) obedient

4. a) contestant b) imminent c) reluctant d) present
   e) intelligent f) defiant

Answers

16 Endings: -cial and -tial

1. special, official, crucial
2. essential, residential, potential, substantial
3. -cial ending: artificial, racial, beneficial, sacrificial
   -tial ending: residential, presidential
4. a) financial b) confidential c) social d) circumstantial

17 Endings: -tious and -cious

1. grace → gracious; space → spacious, malice → malicious
2. -tious: cautious, ambitious
   -cious: suspicious
3. vicious, precious, conscious, delicious, malicious, fictitious

18 Endings: -al -el and -le

1. metal, pedal, hospital, animal
2. a) apple b) capital c) middle d) little e) hotel
3. a) table b) bottle c) camel
4. a) travel, tunnel b) squirrel c) towel

19 Endings: -ant and -ent

1. accident → mishap, experiment → test or trial
   different → diverse or dissimilar
2. a) innocent b) frequent c) decent
3. a) confident b) absent c) contestant d) transparent
   e) reluctant
4. Examples: The food at the Harvest Festival was
   abundant. Samantha was very defiant to her father.
   They could hear the distant rumble of thunder.

20 Endings: -ance and -ence

1. arrogance, assistance, fragrance, importance
2. adolescence, competence, confidence, dependence
3. a) silence b) appearance c) circumference
4. Example: The remembrance service was held in honour
   of all those that had fought in the First World War.
5. a) clearance b) absence c) acceptance d) consequence
   e) guidance

21 Endings: -ancy and -ency

1. hesitancy, expectancy
2. pregnancy, accountancy, flippancy
3. absorbency, consistency, decency
4. a) vacancy b) truancy c) efficiency
5. a) discrepancy b) agency c) infancy d) redundancy
   e) currency

22 Endings: -sure, -ture and -cher

1. picture, nature, adventure, measure
2. creature, archer, enclosure
3. a) treasure b) pleasure c) furniture
4. Examples: The texture of the fabric was very soft.
   The photographer used a long exposure. The preacher
   stood at the front of the church.

23 Endings: -ly

1. gently, cheerfully
2. funnily, friskily, heroically, basically, dramatically, simply,
   humbly, nobly

3. frantically, completely, angrily
4. a) sadly b) grumpily c) beautifully

24 Endings: -ous

1. dangerous, joyous, courageous, nervous
2. spontaneous, vigorous, outrageous, serious
3. a) humorous b) glamorous
4. famous → well-known, various → different
   tremendous → great, enormous → huge

25 Endings: -ation

1. admiration, adoration, information, preparation, sensation
2. imagination, civilisation, consideration, vegetation,
   punctuation
3. a) preparation b) registration c) coronation
4. location → position, nation → country
   celebration → party, donation → contribution

26 Adding suffixes to words ending in -fer

1. preferred, referred, transferred
2. preferring, referring, transferring
3. preference, reference, transference
4. buffer → bumper, differ → contrast, offer → proposal
   infer → suppose

27 Adding suffixes to longer words

1. forgetting, beginning, gardening, limiting
2. admired, allowed, inquired, created
3. Examples: Have you forgotten your homework again?
   They demolished the building with a controlled explosion.
   The interior of the palace was very decorative.
4. a) disturbance b) journalist c) narrator d) thunderous

28 More suffixes

1. sadness, playful, hopeful, happiness, shyness
2. enjoyment, careful, plainness
3. a) plentiful b) penniless c) joyful d) baldness
4. a) bashful b) calmness c) cautiousness

GET IT RIGHT!

29 Homophones

1. a) bawl b) bury c) great d) groan e) meet
2. a) mail b) hear c) knot d) main e) weather
3. verbs: passed, guessed, missed
   nouns: past, guest, mist

30 Silent letters

1. The (k)ni(g)ht pulled the (k)nife from his (k)nee. Could it be –
   he thou(g)ht solem(n)ly – that he was stuck on this
   g(h)astly i(s)land?
2. Examples: The verdict was in doubt. I stayed on a
   remote island. The lamb was born very quickly. The thistle
   had sharp prickles.
3. column, what, whistle, should
4. a) Autumn b) Wednesday c) scissors d) sword
   e) choir f) guest

31 Words with 'ei', 'eigh' or 'ey'

1. v(ei)n, w(eigh), (eigh)t, n(eigh)bour, th(ey)

2. 'ei': reign, sheikh, veil **'eigh'**: freight, weight
   'ey' prey, grey

3. a) obey b) convey c)beige d) sleigh

4. survey → questionnaire
   vein → carries blood to the heart
   neigh → noise a horse makes
   eight → half of 16

32 Words with 'y'

1. The story of Medusa is a myth. Shanaz did 20 bench presses at the gym. The River Nile is in Egypt. Simon was determined to solve the mystery. The oldest of the Seven Wonders of the World is the Great Pyramid.

2. a) dynasty b) mystic c) symbol d) synagogue

3. hymn, synonym, crypt, cygnet, crystal

4. a) lyric b) oxygen

33 Words with 'ough'

1.

'ough' sound	words with that sound
like 'a' in above	thorough
like 'o' in go	although, though
like 'oo' in too	through
like 'off' in offer	cough
like 'uff' in suffer	tough, rough
like 'ow' in flower	plough
like 'aw' in saw	bought, ought

2. a) enough b) dough c) fought d) through

3. a) thought b) nought c) brought

34 Words with 'ei' or 'ie'

1. a) efficient b) conscience c) ancient d) sufficient

2. a) seize b) fields c) foreign d) thief

3. chief, weird, protein

4. sovereign → supreme ruler, counterfeit → fake or forged
   either → one or the other, forfeit → give up
   leisure → free time

35 Words with 'ou'

1. a) touch b) trouble c) young d) double

2. tough → rough or hard, couple → two
   enough → plenty, courage → bravery

3. a) rough b) cousin c) encouraged d) flourish e) nourish

36 Words with 'gue' or 'que'

1. 'gue': tongue, rogue, plague
   'que': antique, unique, plaque

2. a) catalogue b) cheque c) technique d) dialogue

3. monologue → speech by one person
   opaque → not transparent, vague → unclear in meaning
   picturesque → beautiful

4. intrigue, league, unique, grotesque

37 Words with 'sc'

1. a) discipline b) science c) Crescent d) scene e) fascinate

2. obscene → rude or indecent
   transcend → to go beyond or above, adolescent → teenager
   disciple → follower

3. a) descend b) scissors c) scented d) muscles
   e) abscess f) ascent

38 Words with 'ch'

1. a) ache b) anchor c) chaos d) monarch

2. orchid → type of flower, architect → building designer
   stomach → organ in the body
   orchestra → group of musicians

3. scheme, chemistry, mechanic, technical, technology

39 Tricky spellings

1. argument → disagreement, initial → first
   financial → related to money

2. a) provincial b) wholly c) attention

3. Examples: The band had great rhythm. The commercial was shown during half time of the FA Cup Final. Your complaint is duly noted. It is my intention to stand down as Treasurer at the next AGM.

4. a) commercial b) truly c) duly d) intention

Published by Pearson Education Limited, 80 Strand, London, WC2R 0RL.

www.pearsonschools.co.uk

Text © Pearson Education Limited 2016
Edited by Jane Cotter
Typeset by Jouve India Private Limited
Produced by Elektra Media
Original illustrations © Pearson Education Limited 2016
Illustrated by Elektra Media
Cover illustration by Ana Albero

The right of Isabelle Bridger Eames to be identified as author of this work has been asserted by her in accordance with the Copyright, Designs and Patents Act 1988.

First published 2016

19 18 17 16
10 9 8 7 6 5 4 3 2 1

British Library Cataloguing in Publication Data
A catalogue record for this book is available from the British Library.

ISBN 978 1 292 14596 9

Printed in Italy by L.E.G.O. S.p.A.